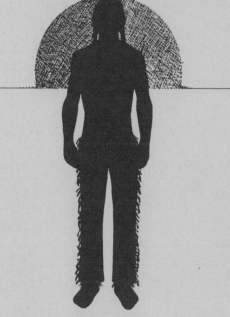

INTRODUCTION

FAR IN THE DISTANT PAST, probably more than 25,000 years ago, the first Americans came to this land.

In those days so much of the world's moisture was locked up in ice that the floor of the Bering Sea lay exposed, forming a landbridge from Siberia to Alaska.

Across this landbridge came nameless bands of nomads hunting animals now extinct. These nomads were the ancestors of the American Indian. Gradually they found their way to every corner of the American continents and there they developed a rich diversity of cultures. In what is now the United States, their settlements extended from the frozen arctic to the swamps of the Everglades; from the eastern woodlands to the western mountains; from the endless grasses of the prairies to the deserts of the southwest. No land was too formidable.

Their languages and their customs differed widely, but often they called themselves "The People." Yet different as they were, they shared a spiritual closeness to all of nature's creatures, to the land, and to the sky. Through stories they taught each new generation about the wonders of the world and man's relation to it. Some of those stories survive today. We have much to learn from The People.

THE PEOPLE

*It is evening. The western sky is set apart
in red. Across the glowing embers of the
campfire, a figure sits, a silhouette against the
sunset colors.*

*It is as if the twilight that is fading from
the sky and land is gathering in about the
campfire. And something more, for now it is
as if all of nature's sounds have paused,
have gathered, attentive and still—waiting...*

MY FRIEND: I am going to tell you the story
of my life, as you wish; but if it were only
the story of my life, I think I would not tell it;
for what is one man that he should make
much of his winters, even when they bend
him like a heavy snow? So many other men
have lived and shall live that story, to be
grass upon the hills.

It is the story of all life that is holy and
is good to tell, and of us two-leggeds sharing
in it with the four-leggeds and the wings
of the air and all green things; for we are but
one people, the children of one mother and
our father is one Spirit.

(Adapted from *Black Elk Speaks*
as told through John G. Neihardt)

The Creation

In the beginning there was nothing, and
only the Great Spirit lived in the void. He
looked around him but there was nothing to
see. He listened, but there was nothing to
hear. There was only the Great Spirit, alone
in nothingness.

The Great Spirit was not lonesome, but as
he moved through the endless time of nothingness, it seemed to him that his power should
be put to use. For what good is power if it is
not used to make a good world, with people
to live in it?

So the Spirit created the great water. Out
of this salty water, he knew, he could bring
forth all life that ever was to be.

"There should be water beings," the
Great Spirit told his power—and now there
were fish swimming in the deep water, then
mussels and snails and crawfish.

2

"There should be creatures that live on the water," the Great Spirit said. And now there were snow geese and mallards, teal and coots, terns and loons. And the Great Spirit could hear the splashing of their feet in the darkness.

"I would like to see these things I have created," said the Great Spirit, and so a great light began to spread across the east, then rose and grew until it reached the middle of the sky and spread a golden glow around the horizon.

And the Great Spirit saw the light, and the birds and fish he had created. "How beautiful it all is," he thought.

Then the snow goose paddled over to where she thought the Great Spirit was, in the space above the waters, and said, "I do not see You, but I know that you exist. I do not know where You are, but I know You must be everywhere. Listen to me, Great Spirit. This is good water that You have made, but birds are not like fish. Sometimes we get tired of swimming. Sometimes we would like to get out of the water."

"Then you shall fly," said the Great Spirit, and all the water birds stirred, then raced skittering along the surface of the water, gathering speed, until they soared into the air and the skies were darkened by their wings.

The loon was first to drop back to the surface of the waters. "Great Spirit," he said, "You have made water for us to swim in, and the sky and light that we might fly. It sounds ungrateful to want something else, yet still we do. When we are tired of swimming and tired of flying, we would like a solid place where we could walk and build our nests."

3

"So be it," said the Great Spirit, "but I must have your help, for by myself I have created water, light, sky air, and the people in and on the waters. By myself I can make only four things. Only with your help can I make more."

"Tell us how we can help," said all the water peoples.

"Let one of you find a piece of land and bring it to me," said the Great Spirit.

So the snow goose, biggest and swiftest of all, plunged downward from the sky, faster than any arrow, and dived into the water. She was gone a long time, and when she broke the surface of the water she was gasping. "Nothing," she sighed sadly, "I brought back nothing."

So the loon tried, and after her, the mallard, And both returned with nothing.

At last there came a little coot, paddling across the water very quietly, dipping his head sometimes to catch a tiny fish. "Great Spirit," said the little coot softly, "when I put my head beneath the water, it seems to me that I see something there, far below. I cannot fly or dive as high and fast and gracefully as my brothers and sisters. But perhaps I can swim down to it. I will swim down the best I know how. May I try, please, Great Spirit?"

"No man can do more than his best," said the Great Spirit. "Try, little brother. See what you can do."

"Thank you, Great Spirit," said the little coot, and he put his head under water and disappeared from sight.

He was gone a long time. And then the Great Spirit and the birds saw a dark speck beneath the water rising towards them. Up, up it came until the coot burst through the surface and shook the water beads from his scalp lock.

"Give us what you have brought," said the Great Spirit, and the little coot let fall from his beak a tiny ball of mud. The Great Spirit rolled the ball of mud between his palms and it began to grow larger, until there was too much for the Great Spirit to hold, but there was nowhere to put it because all was water or air.

"Again, water peoples, you must help me," said the Great Spirit. "One of you must let me place this on your back." All the water

KRISTINE KIRKHAM

creatures came swimming to help. But the mussels and snails and crawfish were too small and lived too deep in the water. The fish were too narrow, and their back fins stuck up through the mud and cut it to pieces. Finally there was only one water person left.

"Grandmother Turtle," said the Great Spirit, "do you think that you can help me?"

"I am very old and very slow," said the turtle, "but I will try." And the Great Spirit piled the mud on her rounded back until Grandmother Turtle was hidden from sight.

"So be it," said the Great Spirit. "Let the earth be known as our Grandmother, and let your Grandmother who carries the earth be the only being who is at home beneath the water, within the earth, or above the ground; the only one who can go anywhere by swimming or by walking as she chooses. And no one shall harm her."

And so it is that Grandmother Turtle and all her descendants must walk very slowly, for they carry the whole weight of the world and all its peoples on their backs.

(Adapted from a Cheyenne myth from *American Indian Mythology* by Alice Marriott and Carol L. Rachlin)

The Sun

At the beginning, on the other side of the world, there was no light, and the four-legged people—the animals—stumbled around in the darkness. Whenever one bumped into another, he would say, "What we need in the world is light." And the other would reply, "Yes, indeed, light is what we badly need."

At last, the animals called a meeting, and gathered together as best they could in the dark.

The red-headed woodpecker said, "I have heard that over on the other side of the world there are people who have light. Perhaps they will give us some."

"If they have all the light there is," the fox said, "they must be greedy people who would not give us any. Maybe we will have to take some light from them."

"Who shall go?" cried everyone, and the animals all began talking at once, arguing about who was strongest and could run fastest.

Finally the possum said, "Let me try. I have a big bushy tail, and I can hide the light inside my fur."

"Good! Good!" said the others, and the possum set out.

As he traveled eastward, the light began to grow and grow until it dazzled his eyes, and the possum squinted to keep out the bright light. And that is why, even today, a possum's eyes are nearly shut and he comes out of his house only at night.

But the possum kept going, all the way to the other side of the world, and there he found the sun. He snatched a little piece of it and hid it in the fur of his fine bushy tail, but the piece of sun was so hot that it burned off all the fur on the possum's tail by the time he got home. And that is why the possum's tail is bare today.

"Oh, my," said the four-leggeds, "our brother has lost his fine bushy tail and still we have no light."

"I'll go," said the buzzard. "I have better sense than to put the sun on my tail. I'll balance it on my beautiful head feathers."

So the buzzard traveled eastward till he came to where the sun was. The guardians of the sun were watching out for thieves now, but the buzzard flew so high they did not see him. Then the buzzard dove straight down out of the sky, the way he does today, and caught a piece of the sun in his claws. He placed the piece of sun on his head and started for home, but the sun was so hot that it burned off all his head feathers, and that is why the buzzard's head is bald today.

Now the people were in despair. "What shall we do?" they cried. "Our brothers have tried hard. They have done their best—everything a man can do. What else can we do so that we will have light?"

"They have done the best a man can do," said a little voice from the grass, "but perhaps this is something a woman can do better than a man."

"Who are you?" everyone asked. "Who is that speaking in a tiny voice and hidden in the grass?"

"I am your Grandmother Spider," she replied. "Perhaps I can bring you light. At least I can try."

And she started eastward, spinning a thread behind her so that she could find her way back.

When Grandmother Spider came to the place of the sun people, she was so little and quiet that no one noticed her. Quietly she spun a web upon the ground and then she reached out gently and took a tiny bit of sun and placed it in her web.

Then carefully pulling the web she went back along the thread that she had spun, back

toward the west, with the sun's light growing and spreading before her.

The animals saw the light rising in the east and they cheered. "Thank you, Grandmother," they said. "We will always honor you and we will always remember what you have done for us."

And that is why, if you will notice, even today a spider's web is shaped like the disk and rays of the sun.

(Adapted from a Cherokee myth from *American Indian Mythology* by Alice Marriott and Carol L. Rachlin)

The Stars

But there was only sun enough to last for half the time, and so in half a day the sun must walk across the sky.

And in those first of days, when the sun each evening lay down and died beyond the western hills and waters, the sky above stood dark and empty.

"We cannot find our way along the paths," the people said. "We are afraid."

So the Creator called a great council—a council of the animals—to help him. And to the creatures he said: "Go to the river and gather up the tiny sparkling stones."

He took one tiny rock himself and placed it in the sky, saying: "This stone will be called a 'star' and it will be the 'home star'—a campfire—that will never move. Look for it if you are lost; it will help you find your way. All the other stars will revolve around it." Then he said to the animals: "Now each of you take some sparkling rocks—as many as you can carry—can draw a picture of yourself in the sky." And each of the creatures set to work. But most of the animals were too small to carry stones enough to complete their pictures, so the Creator gave Coyote a large bag of stones so that Coyote could help the smaller creatures. But Coyote grew impatient. He took the stones and flung them into the sky, which is why some of the star figures are unfinished and why the stars don't all form clear patterns. It was only then that Coyote realized that he had forgotten his own picture—and now there were no rocks left. So Coyote howled, and still and forever a coyote howls at the sky because his picture is not there.

(Adapted from a Hopi myth from *Indian Stories of the Creation* by Julia M. Seton, as presented by Lynn Moroney and Peggie McCracken in a planetarium program)

The Frogs on the Moon

A very long time ago, when the animals still talked to man, there were two sisters who were frogs. The Frog sisters lived in a house in the swamp. Not far away lived two handsome men, Snake and Beaver.

Snake went to the house of the Frog sisters and asked one to marry him. But she said no and called him bad names like "slimy fellow" and "squinty eyes."

Then Beaver went to the house of the Frog sisters and asked the other one to marry him. But she said no and called him bad names like "buck tooth," "big belly," and "flapper tail."

Beaver was so hurt, he went home and cried. "Don't cry," his father said. "It will rain too much if you do."

But Beaver cried harder and much rain fell. Soon the swamp was flooded. The Frog sisters got cold and went to the father of Snake and Beaver. "We want to marry your sons," they said. But the father said, "No, you called my sons bad names."

LAFARNE G. HOLZ

The flood waters carried off the Frog sisters and they floated to the Moon. The Moon invited them into his house to warm themselves by the fire. But they said, "No, we don't want to sit by the fire. We want to sit on your forehead." And with that they jumped on the face of the Moon and spoiled his looks.

You can still see the Frog sisters sitting on the Moon's face even today.

(Adapted from a Lillooet myth from *Indian Tales of North America*, edited by Tristram P. Coffin)

The Great Bear

Once, a long time ago, when the earth was young, there lived a giant bear who was pursued by a giant Indian chief. Day after day, the chief chased the bear until finally one day he caught the bear by its stubby little tail.

The bear roared, but the chief held the bear tightly by its stubby little tail and began to swing the bear around his head. Faster and faster went the bear until his tail was stretched all out of shape. And then the chief hurled the bear up into the sky where the bear got stuck—and he's been going around ever since.

And even today the bear spins in a giant circle around the northern sky—high overhead, then down toward the horizon—with the two bright stars of his body always pointing toward the North Star.

Most stories say that there are four main stars in the body of Bear, and three stars in the tail. But some stories say these three stars are not a tail at all. They are instead three Indians hunting the Bear.

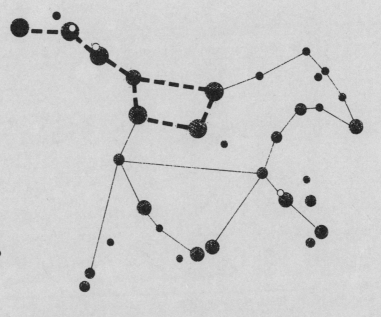

The first Indian carries a bow and arrow to shoot the Bear; the last Indian carries a load of firewood to build a fire; and the middle Indian carries a pot on his shoulder to cook the bear in.

If you look very carefully, you may be able to see the pot—a faint star next to the middle Indian.

The chase began back near the beginning of time when the first Indian shot his arrow and struck the Bear in the side. The wound isn't serious—the Bear has been running ever since and the three pursuing Indians have never gained a step nor gotten close enough for a second shot at the Bear.

Through the night, as the Indians chase the Bear around the sky, the whole sky seems to be turning. But as the weeks pass, each evening the Bear begins the night at a slightly different place in the sky. In the autumn the Bear begins the night low in the northwest.

It is at this season every year, with the Bear crouched low in the northwest, that a strange thing happens. The arrow wound in the side of the Bear opens slightly and a little blood trickles down upon the land. It covers the leaves of the trees and dyes them red— and that is why we have autumn.

We tell this story and so we never forget, even when the weather is warm late into the fall, that when the Bear starts his nightly journey low in the northwest, it is time to store up food for the winter.

The people who cannot see this wisdom in the sky—those people will surely perish in the long cold nights of winter.

(Adapted from Iroquois myths from *Star Lore of All Ages* by William Tyler Olcott)

The Rainbow

A long time ago when the spirits walked the earth, one of them was telling how he helped the winged creatures and the four-leggeds who are brothers and sisters of the Indians.

"I have made feathers for the birds to keep them warm and to flee their enemies and to dance before their mates," the Spirit said.

"I gave the turtle his house, the muskrat his fur coat, and the bear his strong claws and keen nose. To the elk I have given antlers; to the bobcat I have given the color of the trees. I have given great strength to the mountain lion. I know of none I have not helped."

Just then a mother deer looked up. "You have given me to run like the wind," she said, "but how are the little ones to be saved from the sharp teeth of the coyote?"

"I will help you," the Spirit said. He took his brush and paints and colored the fawn with spots of sunlight and ever since the fawn can hide safely in the leaves and shadows.

In the bright days of summer the flowers danced above the grass like a carpet of sparkling jewels. Great was their gift of pleasure to the runners who carried news from village to village. Happy were the feet of the maidens and joyful were the wingeds of the air dancing among the blossoms. But the flowers bowed in sadness.

The Great Spirit was puzzled and he listened.

"Where will we go when the white giant comes from the north and we all must die?" the flowers were saying. "We too make the earth good to look on. Should we not go to a Happy Hunting Ground of our own?"

The Spirit nodded his head smiling. So now after the rainclouds of summer you may see the lovely flowers of last year arching across the heavens in a rainbow.

(A Sioux myth adapted from "Legends of the Sioux," a film by Charles W. Nauman for the South Dakota Department of Highways)

The Four Seasons

Long, long ago, in the days of our grand-fathers' memories, there was a man to whom the Great Spirit showed the many different pathways of the sun—paths that made things hot and other paths that made things cold. It was the task of this man to guide the sun.

But the people on earth were never satisfied. They always complained about the weather. The days were too hot—or too cold. There was not enough rain—or too much rain.

Now this man who watched over the sun had four children—all boys. And the four brothers were always quarreling. Finally the noise of the people on earth and the noise of his four sons were too much and the man decided that he would never please anyone. So he told his four children that they would have to watch over the sun. Each could do with the sun whatever he wanted, but each of the brothers would have the same amount of time, with the youngest brother going first.

The youngest boy was a gentle child, and as he journeyed with the sun, he slowed to admire the trees and flowers, and to whistle with the birds. So the plants grew, the birds built nests, and the earth put on a green-all-over cover. If the sun was too hot, the boy called the Wind Man to bring the Cloud Man to shield and cool the land. These were the days of spring.

The days passed and the youngest brother forgot that his time was up to have things as he wanted them. So the second brother came to meet him and the youngest brother showed him the things that he had done. The new watchman of the sun admired all the trees and birds' nests. And young birds flew and the plants gave fruit.

But the sun was hot and the younger brothers grew tired and went to sleep. And the earth—all over green—turned yellow. These were the days of summer.

Now the third brother, whose turn it was to have the days as he wanted them, was angry and sent the Wind Man to find his younger brothers, and the wind screeched to awaken them. Then the third brother took

Autumn Kachina of Pueblo Indians

a stick and beat Wind Man because he was not working and the sun was too hot and there were no storms.

The Wind went close to the earth, trying to hide. And because of Wind Man the leaves and cover of the earth dried up and the birds were frightened and sang no more. These were the days of autumn.

Then the third boy went home and gave his turn to the oldest of the four brothers.

Now the oldest brother was hard and over-bearing. He told the sun that he was on the wrong road and ordered him to take the southern, coldest path. The Wind Man and his brother the Cloud Man were working very hard but because the sun walked so far away there was little heat and so the wind was cold and what fell from the clouds was hard.

The ground called out to the oldest brother, but he would not listen. When anything tried to grow through the frozen ground, the oldest brother stepped on it. These were the days of winter.

And now those days were over and the Great Spirit called the oldest brother and sent him home. It was time for the youngest brother to take his turn again.

A year had passed. The sun was high, then low, then once more high in the heavens. And the people on the earth were still complaining. Some liked one brother; some liked another. So the Great Spirit decided that the four brothers should always take their turns, doing just what they had done.

And that is why we have four seasons.

(Adapted from a Papago myth from *Long Ago Told* by Harold Bell Wright)

KRISTINE KIRKHAM
Ancient Indian City of Cahokia, Illinois

Indian Astronomical Monuments

The everchanging pathways of the sun were known to the grandfathers of our fathers' grandfathers long before our people lived where they live today. A thousand years ago, across the Father-of-Waters from the modern city of St. Louis was the great Indian city of Cahokia. It was a trade and farming center. People came from 500 miles away up and down the great central river system to buy and sell—and to see the city.

Inside and near the walls of Cahokia were more than 100 mounds of every sort: mounds topped by homes and storehouses, huge mounds for ceremonies, mounds for sacrifices, and mounds for the burial of chiefs.

Beyond the walls of the inner city, to the northwest, lay a clearing on which the early people had erected 48 tall wooden posts—tree trunks—in an immense circle more than a hundred yards across. At dawn and dusk, a sunwatcher may have ascended a post near the center of the circle, there to observe where

the sun rose and set along the horizon. When the sun rose farthest to the north of east at the beginning of summer, that special point along the horizon was marked by a post in the circle over which the sunwatcher could sight. And so it was that the rising and setting sun in spring and fall and winter were marked also.

Cahokia had a solar observatory to chart the seasons. Here was set a calendar for farming—when to plant and when to harvest—based not on the 12 moons in the passing year, but on a counting of the 365 days that surround a growing season.

(Based on material in *The First Americans* by Robert Claiborne; Time-Life Emergence of Man series)

And this 365-day cycle in a year was known not only to the people of the eastern plains and woodlands, but was known to the western people as well.

In the Big Horn Mountains of northern Wyoming, on a high plateau, there is a pattern laid out on the ground in rocks and mounds. It is 80 feet in diameter. There, more than 200 years ago, people may have come to stand at the beginning of the summer to honor

15

Photo by JOHN A EDDY
Big Horn Medicine Wheel, Wyoming

the sun in the midst of its glory, rising far to the north of east to stand high in the sky at the beginning of the summer season—the season of growth and abundance. This sacred place has been called Medicine Wheel because it was a monument that honored the sun and great spirits above and the powers that dwell in nature.

(Based on research by John A. Eddy: "Astronomical Alignment of the Big Horn Medicine Wheel," *Science*, volume 184, number 4141 (7 June 1974), pages 1035-1043)

As our people watched and grew to know the sky so long ago, they saw there many signs; many strange occurrences.

Our people, who lived in the standing-up country, the painted deserts of the southwest, left on cave and canyon walls a thousand years ago paintings and carvings of their observations, perhaps even of a rare and startling sight—suddenly there in the heavens was a new star which outshone every other starlike object.

It was, in modern counting, the early morning hours of July 4, 1054 A.D. The object was a supernova—the explosion of a giant star. We could not know that at the time, nor that of all the peoples on the earth, perhaps only the Chinese, the Japanese, and we, the first Americans, cared enough about the sky to notice and record this dazzling sight.

Even when morning came, the new star could still be seen in daylight.

And next night late, towards dawn, the great new star rose again, and now beside it stood the waning crescent moon, just a little to the north—the two brightest nighttime objects ever visible in the memory of man.

What thoughts they had, our old people did not leave us, but it may be they left behind their fascination and their awe, for still today on cave and canyon walls you may see our people's record of the crescent moon and the great star.

(Based on research by William C. Miller: "Two Possible Astronomical Pictographs Found in Northern Arizona," *Plateau* (Museum of Northern Arizona), volume 27, number 1 (April 1955); and research by John C. Brandt et al: "Possible Rock Art Records of the Crab Nebula Supernova in the Western United States," *Archaeoastronomy in Pre-Columbian America*, edited by A.F. Aveni)

Long Sash (Orion)

But now there came a time of troubles. A new enemy—attacking villages, stealing animals, killing families. It was worse then ever before.

And then Long Sash came forward. "Take us away from here," the people begged him. "Lead us to a new land, where we can live peacefully."

And Long Sash spoke: "My people, life is hard here, I know, but it will not be easy anywhere. There will be dangers on the way if we travel. Think, and be sure you want to take that risk."

And the people said: "We will face any hardships. Only lead us away from this dark country, to a place where we may have light and life of our own."

So Long Sash set forth and the people followed him. They set their feet on the Endless Trail that stretches like a faint white band across the sky. This was the road they were going to follow out of the land that once was theirs towards a new place of their own.

Westward they went until at last Long Sash brought them to a country which was so new that even he had never been there before. Children were born and old people died and still they journeyed onward.

But now the people quarreled among themselves, exchanging blows. And Long Sash said to them: "This must stop. You are hurting yourselves worse than your enemies hurt you. If you are to come to a place of your own, there can never be violence among you. You must decide—whether you will follow me or take another trail."

North and east of Long Sash are two bright stars. It is there that the people sat down to rest and to make up their minds. The white man calls those stars Gemini—the Twins. To us they are the Place of Decision, and people look up to them for help today when they come to turning points in their lives. Those two stars remind us that real decisions are seldom easy—sometimes both paths look equally bright—yet we must choose, and go on.

And the people followed Long Sash, with good hearts and love for each other.

But now Long Sash was growing tired. His own heart was empty and doubting. And Long Sash spoke to the unseen voices and said: "Show me a sign, fathers and mothers. My people are tired and I am growing old. Give me a word to tell me we are on the right path and will soon reach our home." Then Long Sash dropped down where he had been sitting and his eyes closed. And his people grew more and more frightened.

At last Long Sash opened his eyes. He looked at the people gathered around him and spoke: "Do not be afraid. The worst part of our journey is over, and we will soon reach the end. Many people will reach this Place of Doubt in their lives. When that happens, you should pray to the above persons, your fathers and mothers, for help and guidance. And to remind you of that, I will leave my headdress here in the sky, where you can look up and see it."

And where he placed his headdress, it became a bright comforting cluster of stars. The white man calls those stars the Pleiades.

And so the people went on traveling, and all the story of their journey is told in the stars above. At last the people came to the end of their journey, to the Middle Place which was to be their home forever.

(Adapted from a Tewa myth from *American Indian Mythology* by Alice Marriott and Carol L. Rachlin; where the "headdress" star cluster is identified as the faint Praesepe cluster in Cancer)

The Winter When the Stars Fell

But the Middle Place was not to be their home forever. For now it was the Winter When the Stars Fell. The white men said it was 1833—November 12. It was our Month of the Snapping Trees.

The evening started quietly, the stars and constellations turning slowly silently overhead. Every now and then a meteor—like a falling star—would streak across the heavens—as on any evening.

But this was to be no ordinary night. For now there were falling stars everywhere, and then more—thousands every minute. Beyond all counting. The four-leggeds and the winged ones stirred and moaned and no one slept that night. Our wise men said it was a bad sign—that the falling stars were like the white men falling by the thousands upon our land—coming at first a few at a time but now coming in great streams, pouring from the east upon the lands promised to us for all time. And still they came.

And our wise men were right, for we heard that the white man's president, who was proud of fighting Indians, said that very year:

Those Indian tribes cannot exist near our settlements. They have neither the intelligence, the industry, the moral habits, nor a desire for improvement. Established in the midst of our superior race, they must necessarily yield to the force of circumstances and ere long disappear.

(Andrew Jackson, wording edited slightly)

Could the ashes of the council fires that once stretched across this continent be given the power to speak, what stories they would tell: stories about the long ago time when the world was young, when animals could speak and share their wisdom with us. The world has grown older now, bowed with many winter snows. The ground is no longer young. It is the dust and blood of our ancestors. But the stories are like the stars; they never change. There must always be the stories.

The Morning Star and the Northern Lights

Old Chief Morning Star had only one son. Young Morning Star worried his father because he would not play with the other boys. Instead, he would leave home for days at a time, always going towards the north.

One day the Old Chief followed his son. Young Morning Star took a strange path northward—the Spirit's Path—the Milky Way.

But when the Old Chief set foot upon the sacred path, suddenly he could not see or hear.

When he opened his eyes, he was in a land of strange lights. There the people all were wearing belts of rainbow light and colored lights upon their heads. All through the night they played a game with a ball made of changing colors.

And as the Old Chief watched the players of the northern land dodge and leap and chase the ball, he saw his son, Young Morning Star, foremost among the players, wearing the most vivid lights.

When the game was over, Morning Star went home with his father and all his people were glad because the morning star was with them again—brightening the colored skies of dawn.

And when Morning Star cannot be seen, the people know that he is in the northern land of color. So when the special game with lights is played, and the Northern Lights leap and dance about the sky, the people know that Morning Star lives on and will return again.

(Adapted from a Wabanaki myth from *Indian Tales of North America*, edited by Tristram P. Coffin)

The voice paused. There was scarcely any twilight left. The dying fire seemed to draw from all directions inward a cool night wind, and on that wind came voices.

The Meeting

Now this is the day.
Our child
Into the daylight
You will go forth.

Preparing for your day,
We have passed our days.

Our child, it is your day.
May your path be fulfilled
Reaching to the height of the sun.

When your path is fulfilled,
In your thoughts may we live,
To this end:
May you help us all to finish our paths.

(Zuni: adaptation of Prayer Spoken While Presenting an Infant to the Sun)

Photo by EDWARD S CURTIS

The utmost good faith shall always be observed towards the Indians; their lands and property shall never be taken from them...

(U.S. Congress, 1789)

O our Mother the Earth, O our Father the
    Sky,...
Weave for us a garment of brightness;
May the warp be the white light of morning,
May the weft be the red light of evening,
May the fringes be the falling rain,
May the border be the standing rainbow.
Thus weave for us a garment of brightness,
That we may walk fittingly where birds sing,
That we may walk fittingly where grass is
    green,
O our Mother the Earth, O our Father the
    Sky.

(Tewa: Song of the Sky Loom)

No white person or persons shall be permitted to settle upon, to occupy, or to pass through any portion of this territory without the consent of the Indians.

(Treaty of 1868; wording edited slightly)

Up on the Madison Fork, the white men found much of the yellow metal that they worship—the yellow metal that makes them crazy.

(Black Elk—Sioux)

One does not sell the earth upon which the people walk.

(Crazy Horse—Sioux)

The soldiers cut down the trees; they kill the buffalo; and when I see that, my heart feels like bursting... Has the white man become a child that he should recklessly kill and not eat?

(Satanta—Kiowa)

Damn any man who sympathizes with Indians! I have come to kill Indians, and believe it is right and honorable to use any means under God's heaven to kill Indians.

(General John M. Chivington)

We were born naked and have been taught to hunt and live on game. You tell us that we must learn to farm, live in one house, and take on your ways. Suppose the people living beyond the great sea should come and tell you that you must stop farming, and kill your cattle, and take your houses and lands, what would you do. Would you not fight them?

(Gall—Sioux)

They talked and talked for days, but it was just like the wind blowing in the end.

(Black Elk—Sioux)

Brother, you say there is but one way to worship and serve the Great Spirit. If there is but one religion, why do you white people differ so much about it? We also have a religion which was given to our forefathers. It teaches us to be thankful for all the favors we receive and to love each other. We never quarrel about religion. Brother, we do not wish to destroy your religion, or take it from you; we only want to enjoy our own.

(Red Jacket—Seneca; wording edited slightly)

You say that you want to put us on a reservation, to build us houses... I do not want them. I was born upon the prairie, where the wind blew free and there was nothing to break the light of the sun... I know every stream and every wood between the Rio Grande and the Arkansas... I have lived like my fathers before me, and, like them, I lived happily.

(Ten Bears—Comanche)

A warrior
I have been.
Now it is all over.
A hard time
I have.

(Sitting Bull—Sioux)

The people were hungry and in despair. The white men gave us less than half the beef cattle they promised us in the treaty, and these cattle were very poor. We got more lies than cattle, and we could not eat lies.

(Black Elk—Sioux)

Photo by EDWARD S CURTIS

My children,
When at first I liked the whites,
I gave them corn,
I gave them fruits.

Father have pity on me,
I am crying for thirst,
All is gone,
I have nothing to eat.

My children—my children...
The whites are crazy.

We shall live again,
We shall live again.

(Songs from the Ghost Dance
Religion—Arapaho & Comanche)

The only good Indians I ever saw were dead.
(General Philip Sheridan)

I am tired of fighting. Our chiefs are killed... The little children are freezing to death. My people, some of them, have run away to the hills and have no blankets, no food. No one knows where they are—perhaps they are freezing to death. I want to have time to look for my children and see how many of them I can find. Maybe I shall find them among the dead. Hear me, my chiefs, I am tired. My heart is sad and sick. From where the sun now stands I will fight no more forever.

(Chief Joseph—Nez Percé)

And now the wind and voices ceased. The figure had not moved as he had spoken. He had not moved as the windsong spoke. Yet now, imperceptibly, his gaze was fixed upon the stars. And as he spoke, his arms spread slowly outward, upward to the sky.

Grandfather, Great Spirit, once more behold me on earth and lean to hear my feeble voice. All things belong to you—the two-leggeds, the four-leggeds, the wings of the air, and all green things that live. Therefore I am sending a voice, Great Spirit, my Grandfather.

I recall the great vision you sent us. A little root of that sacred tree still lives. Nourish it that it may leaf and bloom and fill with singing birds. Hear me, not for myself, but for my people. Hear me in my sorrow, for I may never call again. O make my people live.

(Black Elk—Sioux; wording edited slightly)

He looked down again, into the campfire, across it, and beyond...

Chief Joseph

On Indian Mythology

The legends of the Indians are out of the past older than anyone knows. They are simple legends born of the ways of people who have lived as brothers and sisters of all of nature's creatures. Their roots are one with the trees. They talk with the sun and wind and the rain and they know the language of the birds and animals.

All people who have ever lived on this beautiful earth have legends. All have great men. When the legends die, something within the people dies.

To the Indians our legends are something that cannot be measured in gold. No people's legends can. This is a great and beautiful country and it will stay that way as long as people have stories to remind them to live for greatness and beauty.

(Adapted from "Legends of the Sioux," a film by Charles W. Nauman for the South Dakota Department of Highways)

The Milky Way

And late at night, as the white fire coals deepen into black, we tell of our great souls. Silent were their footsteps through the pine forests, across the buffalo grass, and into the canyons. Unerring in direction. With their lives they blazed a trail for their people to follow with honor.

And when their footsteps brought them to that chasm beyond which men venture once only, they vanished from our midst. Likely it is we shall not see their equal again.

But as they left their work and spirit forever with us their people, so even now as they journey on, they leave an imperishable mark upon the sky, for there, arching across the heavens is the pathway of souls.

We do not know where their journey leads. Nor do we know what sights they may behold. And in the night each bright star is a campfire blazing in the sky where they have paused in their journey to look down on us, their people, as we huddle for warmth around the campfire.

(Adapted from an Algonquin myth from *Star Lore of All Ages* by William Tyler Olcott)